# English

## made easy

### Preschool
### ages 3–5
### Early Writing

**Author** Su Hurrell

## Certificate

Congratulations to 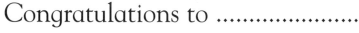 ......................................................
(write your name here)
for successfully finishing this book.

 *You're a star!*

# Drawing curvy lines

Trace over the line with your pencil, then keep going.
Fill the page with curvy lines.

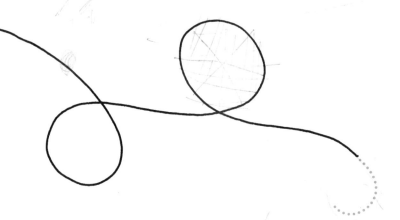

Colour in the shapes that you have made.

# Drawing straight lines

Trace over the line with your pencil, then keep going.
Fill the page with straight lines.

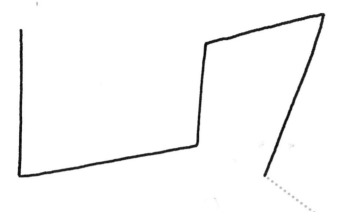

Colour in the shapes that you have made.

# Moving left to right

Help each animal find a home.
Draw a line from the animal to its home.

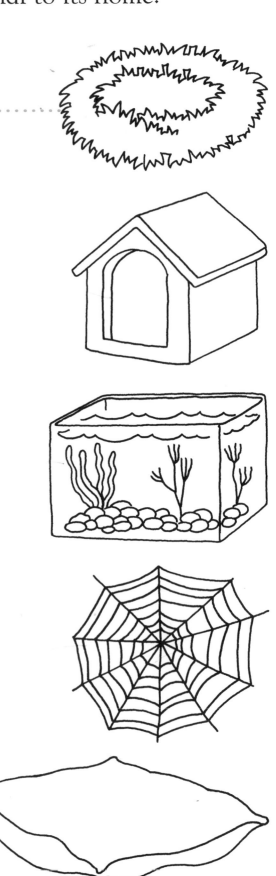

Help each animal find its dinner.
Draw a line from the animal to its food.

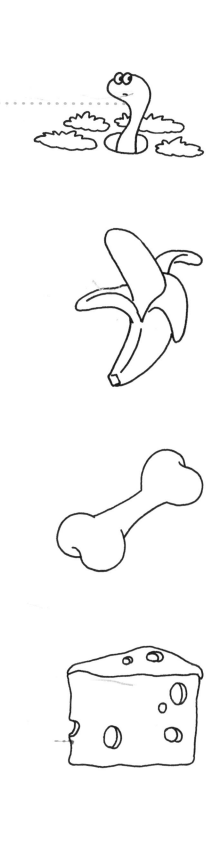

# Moving left to right

Follow each dotted line with your finger,
then draw a line over the dots.

# Follow each dotted line with your finger, then draw a line over the dots.

# Practising circles

Join the dots to finish the picture.
Start at each big dot, and follow the arrow.

# Practising straight lines

Join the dots to finish the pictures.
Start at each big dot, and follow the arrow.

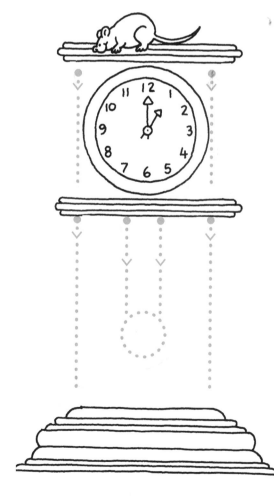

# Practising wavy lines

Join the dots to finish the picture.
Start at each big dot, and follow the arrows.

# Practising curvy lines

Join the dots to finish the picture.
Start at each big dot, and follow the arrows.

# Practising curves

Join the dots to finish the picture.
Start at each big dot, and follow the arrow.

Join the dots to finish the picture.
Start at each big dot, and follow the arrow.

# Creating patterns

Trace over the line, then finish the pattern by joining the dots.

Copy the pattern here.

Now trace and finish this pattern.

Copy the pattern.

Trace and finish the pattern.

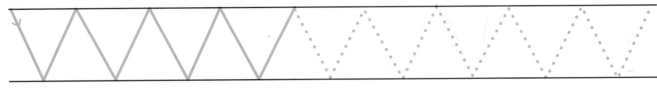

Copy the pattern.

Trace and finish the pattern.

Copy the pattern.

Trace and finish the pattern.

Copy the pattern.

Trace and finish the pattern.

Copy the pattern.

# Writing letters: c and o

Join the dots. Start at the big dot, and follow the arrow.

C  C  C  C  C  C  C

Copy the letter here.

Now join the dots to finish the picture.

Join the dots. Start at the big dot, and follow the arrow.

O  O  O  O  O  O  O

Copy the letter here.

# a and d

Join the dots. Start at the big dot, and follow the arrows.

a a a a a a a

Copy the letter here.

Now join the dots to finish the picture.

Join the dots. Start at the big dot, and follow the arrows.

d d d d d d d

Copy the letter here.

# g and q

Join the dots. Start at the big dot, and follow the arrows.

g g g g g g g

Copy the letter here.

Now join the dots to finish the picture.

Join the dots. Start at the big dot, and follow the arrows.

q q q q q q q

Copy the letter here.

# e and s

Join the dots. Start at the big dot, and follow the arrows.

e    e    e    e    e    e

Copy the letter here.

Now join the dots to finish the picture.

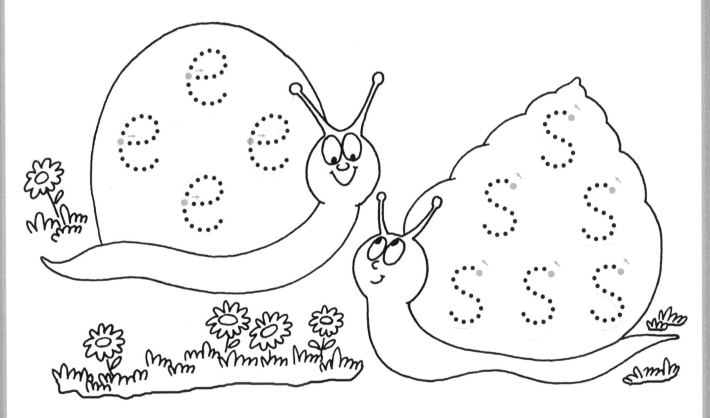

Join the dots. Start at the big dot, and follow the arrow.

s    s    s    s    s    s

Copy the letter here.

# p and b

Join the dots. Start at the big dot, and follow the arrows.

p  p  p  p  p  p  p

Copy the letter here.

Now join the dots to finish the picture.

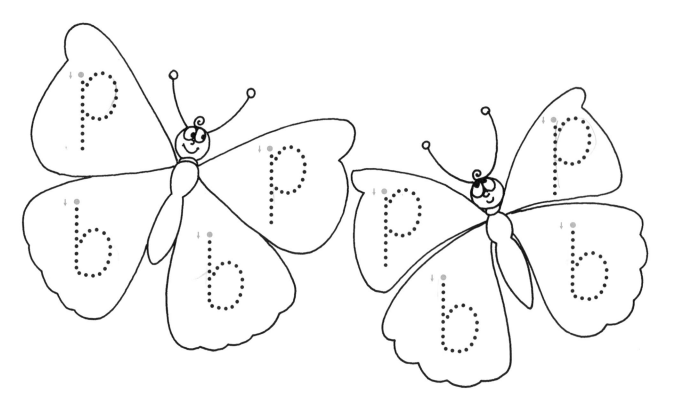

Join the dots. Start at the big dot, and follow the arrows.

b  b  b  b  b  b  b

Copy the letter here.

# l and j

Join the dots. Start at the big dot, and follow the arrow.

l l l    l l l l l l

Copy the letter here.

Now join the dots to finish the picture.

Join the dots. Start at the big dot, and follow the arrow.

j j j    J J J J J J

Copy the letter here.

# i and t

Join the dots. Start at the big dot, and follow the arrow.

i i i i i i i i

Copy the letter here.

Now join the dots to finish the picture.

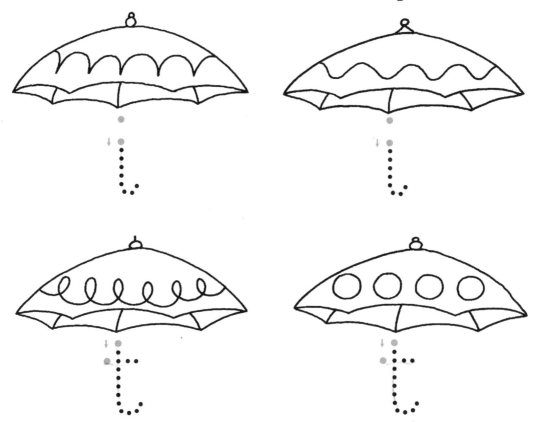

Join the dots. Start at the big dot, and follow the arrows.

t t t t t t t t

Copy the letter here.

# k and f

Join the dots. Start at the big dot, and follow the arrows.

k k k k k k k

Copy the letter here.

Now join the dots to finish the picture.

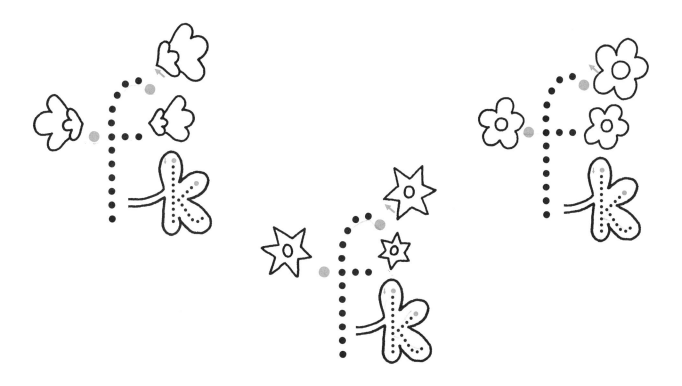

Join the dots. Start at the big dot, and follow the arrows.

f f f f f f f

Copy the letter here.

# r and n

Join the dots. Start at the big dot, and follow the arrows.

r r r r r r r r r

Copy the letter here.

Now join the dots to finish the picture.

Join the dots. Start at the big dot, and follow the arrows.

n n n n n n n

Copy the letter here.

# h and m

Join the dots. Start at the big dot, and follow the arrows.

h  h  h  h  h  h  h

Copy the letter here.

Now join the dots to finish the picture.

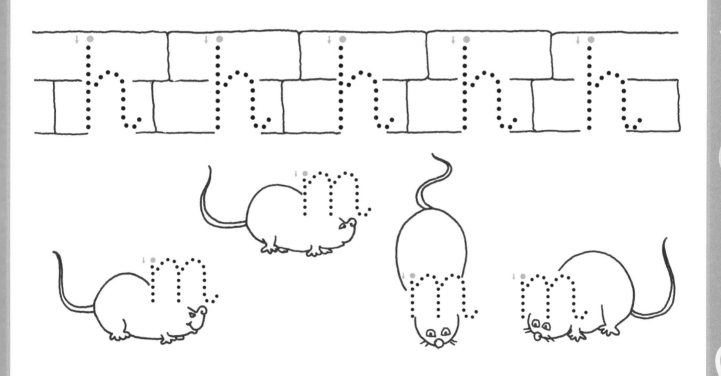

Join the dots. Start at the big dot, and follow the arrows.

m  m  m  m  m  m  m

Copy the letter here.

# u and y

Join the dots. Start at the big dot, and follow the arrows.

u u u u u u u

Copy the letter here.

Now join the dots to finish the picture.

Join the dots. Start at the big dot, and follow the arrows.

y y y y y y y

Copy the letter here.

# v and w

Join the dots. Start at the big dot, and follow the arrows.

V  V  V  V  V  V  V

Copy the letter here.

Now join the dots to finish the picture.

Join the dots. Start at the big dot, and follow the arrows.

W  W  W  W  W  W

Copy the letter here.

# x and z

Join the dots. Start at the big dot, and follow the arrows.

X X X X X X X

Copy the letter here.

Now join the dots to finish the picture.

Join the dots. Start at the big dot, and follow the arrows.

Z Z Z Z Z Z Z

Copy the letter here.

# The alphabet

Now you can write all your letters.
Copy each letter by joining the dots.

a b c d e f g

a b c d e f g

h i j k l m n

h i j k l m n

o p q r s t u

o p q r s t u

v w x y z

v w x y z

The letters are in alphabetical order.

29

# Write your name

Find the first letter in your name in the box below, and draw a (ring) around it. Then copy the letter onto the line at the bottom of the page. Now find the next letter. Keep going till you have written your name.

a b c d e f

g h i j k l

m n o p q r

s t u v w x

y z

My name is

30

# Write sentences

Copy the words below. Leave a finger space between each word. Draw a picture of yourself in the frame.

This is me.

This is a monster.

# Practise sentences

These words use all the letters that you have learned.
Copy the words, and remember to leave a finger space
between each word.

The  quick  brown  fox

jumps  over  the  lazy  dog.

# Notes for Parents

This book is designed to help your child develop the early skills that are needed when learning to write small letters. The fun writing activities group letters together in "families" according to similarities in their shape and formation, rather than follow alphabetical order. By tracing and drawing lines and writing letter shapes, children will develop the correct formation of letters, which is the basis for good handwriting in the future.

## Content

By working through this book, your child will learn:
- to develop fine muscle control of his or her hand and fingers;
- to make fluent marks on paper;
- to develop eye-and-hand co-ordination;
- to write from left to right, starting at the top of the page;
- to draw the basic patterns that form letters;
- to write lower-case letters in the correct way;
- to write letters with flicks in preparation for joining up letters later on;
- to recognise letter shapes and learn their names;
- to understand that letters go together to create words;
- to recognise words and understand that spaces are needed between words for them to make sense.

## How to help your child with writing

In the course of everyday life, it is important that your child sees both you and other adults writing for a purpose. Encourage your child to join in this activity whenever you can, and praise his or her achievements. Even though your child's early writing attempts may look like scribbles, he or she can share in the writing of a shopping list, sign a greetings card or write a note to grandparents. All of these valuable writing opportunities will help your child to develop an understanding of the power of the written word.

Before your child begins writing in this book, play writing games without using a pencil. At bath time, encourage him or her to use a finger to draw patterns in the bubbles or on a steamed-up mirror or window. When outdoors, draw shapes in the sand on the beach or in the sandpit. These activities will help your child to develop fluent, continuous movements in preparation for using a pencil.

## Holding a pencil

When drawing and writing, help your child to hold the pencil correctly. The position is the same for both right- and left-handed children. If you are not sure which is your child's dominant hand, observe your child closely when playing. Whichever hand he or she uses to feed teddy, wind up toys or pick up small things is likely to be the dominant hand. Alternatively, you could place a cardboard tube in front of your child and ask him or her to look through it as if it were a telescope. Your child will probably pick it up with the dominant hand and place it to the dominant eye. Sometimes the dominant eye and hand will not be on the same side, but this doesn't usually present problems for a child when developing early literacy skills.

## Pencil grip

Your child should pick up the pencil in the dominant hand and hold it between the thumb and first finger. The second finger goes beneath the pencil to support it. Make sure that the pencil is not gripped too tightly and not held too close to the tip. It should rest at an angle of 45 degrees between the first finger and the thumb. If your child has problems, it can help if you make a grip for the pencil. Mould a small piece of Plasticine into a three-sided pyramid, and push the pencil through the middle – this will encourage your child to place his or her fingers correctly.

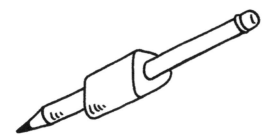 

# How to use this book

### Writing materials

Before beginning the activities in this book, make sure that you have suitable pencils and colouring pencils or felt-tip pens ready.

Your child should have a sharpened pencil, which is not too pointed. A soft lead pencil (2B) is preferable for the writing activities. If the pencil is too hard, your child's writing may be difficult to see on the page, which could lead to frustration.

Your child will need colouring pencils or felt-tip pens – not the type that bleed through paper, as they will spoil subsequent pages. Avoid crayons, as these may be too thick for accurately colouring the pictures and could lead to frustration.

## Getting the most from the activities

Always work through the book in page order. The book progresses from lines to patterns, on to letters and then words. It is important not to miss out any of these stages as the contents have been carefully planned to take your child through a progression of early writing skills. If your child is struggling with the activities, don't worry. He or she may not be ready for this book or may only be able to do the first few activities. If this happens, leave the book for a while, and continue to let your child draw shapes without a pencil. Later on, return to the book, recapping on any pages he or she has already completed.

Working through the activities in this book should be an enjoyable shared experience for both you and your child, so choose a moment when you have time to concentrate and your child is not too tired or hungry. Read the instructions aloud, making sure that your child understands what he or she is expected to do for each activity.

Don't spend too long on each activity session – it's better to keep it short and fun and to let your child get a feel for the writing skills involved. Celebrate your child's success, and build his or her confidence by giving plenty of praise and encouragement along the way.

If your child has enjoyed a particular activity or is having some difficulty with it, try doing some additional practice on scrap paper. You may find it helpful to have some extra paper to hand before you start your activity sessions.

When your child has completed the book, continue to provide plenty of opportunities for him or her to practise writing.

# Page-by-page notes

## Pages 2 and 3 – Drawing curvy lines and Drawing straight lines

These activities encourage your child to create fluent lines on the page. Your child should keep an even pressure and try not to take the pencil off the page until he or she has completed a scribble pattern.

pages 2 and 3

## Pages 4 and 5 – Moving left to right

These activities help your child to practise pencil movement from left to right. Before using a pencil, encourage your child to trace the path with a finger. The aim is for your child to draw a continuous line from left to right and to get used to the feeling of moving across the page.

pages 4 and 5

## Pages 6 and 7 – Moving left to right

Some children may find these activities easier than drawing straight lines from left to right. Your child should practise first by tracing the different paths with a finger. Talk about the pictures and patterns he or she is making.

pages 6 and 7

## Pages 8 and 9 – Practising circles and Practising straight lines

On page 8, your child practises forming an anti-clockwise circle, which will give him or her confidence when creating rounded letter shapes. Your child may find it quite natural to draw a circle, but it is important that he or she begins on the big dot and follows the arrow around in an anti-clockwise direction. On page 9, your child is introduced to drawing vertical lines in a downwards direction, which is an important aspect of letter formation. It might help to practise both these movements with a finger and then on some spare paper before tackling the activities on the page.

pages 8 and 9

## Pages 10, 11, 12 and 13 – Practising wavy lines, Practising curvy lines and Practising curves

On these pages, your child joins the dots starting with the big dot to form wavy or curvy lines. Encourage your child to practise a fluid movement and to keep the pencil moving. Talk about the shapes and patterns that your child is creating. These pictures are also fun for your child to colour and complete.

pages 10 and 11

## Pages 14 and 15 – Creating patterns

These patterns are found in letter shapes, and they also reinforce left-to-right pencil movement. Trace the patterns first with a finger or practise on some spare paper. Don't forget to praise your child's efforts and celebrate his or her achievements.

pages 12 and 13

## Pages 16 to 29 – Writing letters

Children should develop the skill of writing letters in several stages:

1. Begin by tracing the letter shape with a finger.
2. Write over the letter shape on the page. Begin with the big dot and follow the direction of the arrow(s).
3. Copy the letter by writing between the sets of lines.

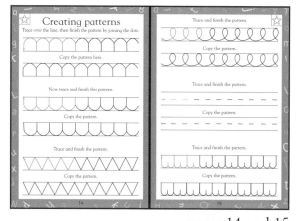

pages 14 and 15

When writing the letters, call each one by its name, stressing to your child that it is the name of the letter. This book concentrates on letter formation and not the phonetic sound of each letter. Always describe and talk about the movement being made as each letter is formed. You can describe each letter movement as outlined on the following pages or create your own description to suit your child.

## Pages 16 and 17 – Writing letters: c and o and Writing letters: a and d

c – start at the top, and then go halfway
around;

o – start at the top, and then go all the way
around;

a – start at the top, go all the way around,
then down and flick;

d – start on the dot, go all the way around,
up and down and flick.

Some letters, such as *a* and *d*, have flicks.
These are included to help with joining up
letters, which is tackled at a later stage.

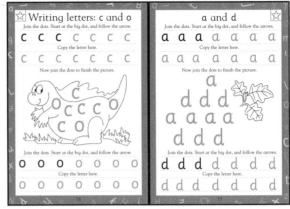

pages 16 and 17

## Pages 18 and 19 – Writing letters: g and q and Writing letters: e and s

g – start at the top, go all the way around,
then down and around;

q – start at the top, go all the way around,
then down and flick;

e – start at the dot, go across, then up, and
then halfway around;

s – go around and back again.

pages 18 and 19

## Page 20 and 21 – Writing letters: p and b and Writing letters: l and j

These letters are created in one continuous
movement without lifting the pencil (apart
from the dot).

p – go from top to bottom, bottom to top, and
all the way around;

b – go from top to bottom, up and all the way
around;

l – go from top to bottom and flick;

j – go from top to bottom, down and around,
then add a dot.

pages 20 and 21

## Pages 22 and 23 – Writing letters: i and t and Writing letters: k and f

i – go top to bottom, flick, then add a dot;

t – go top to bottom, flick, and then go across;

k – go top to bottom, in then out, and then flick;

f – go around and all the way down, and then across.

pages 22 and 23

## Pages 24 and 25 – Writing letters: r and n and Writing letters: h and m

These letters are made in one continuous movement.

r – go top to bottom, up, and then just over the top;

n – go top to bottom, up and over, and then flick;

h – go top to bottom, up and over, and then flick;

m – go top to bottom, up and over, up and over, and flick.

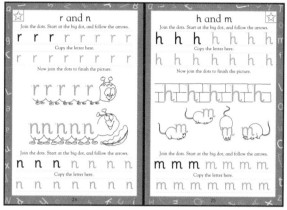

pages 24 and 25

## Pages 26 and 27 – Writing letters: u and y and Writing letters: v and w

Once again, these letters are made in one continuous movement without the pencil leaving the page.

u – go down and around, up and down and flick;

y – go down and around, up and down and around;

v – go down and up;

w – go down and up, down and up.

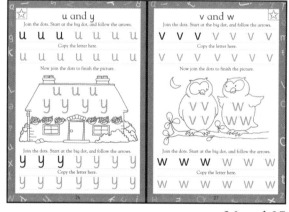

pages 26 and 27

## Pages 28 and 29 – Writing letters:
## x and z and The alphabet

x – go across and down, and across and down;

z – go across, then down and across, then back across. This letter should be made in one continuous movement.

On page 29, the 26 letters are presented in alphabetical order. This provides more writing practice for your child. The letters are written on the sets of lines to help children with the proportions of the different letters, especially the tall ones and those with tails.

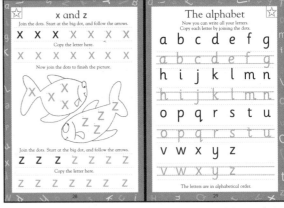

pages 28 and 29

## Pages 30 and 31 – Write your name and Write sentences

Help your child to identify the letters in his or her name and copy them onto the page. If you want to add a capital letter at the beginning of the name, explain to your child that capital letters are written in a different way from small letters.

On page 31, your child can practise copying some whole words put together in short sentences. Talk about the letter shapes and point out how letters are put together in groups to make words. When copying words, it is important to leave a space in between them. Ask your child to place a finger from the non-writing hand at the end of each word. He or she can then start to write the next word after the finger, creating an adequate space between words.

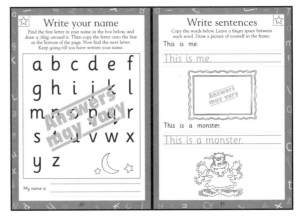

pages 30 and 31

page 32

## Page 32 – Practise sentences

This last activity features all the letters of the alphabet in a funny sentence for your child to copy. There is also a large, fun picture to colour.